The story of my life

REFLECTIONS ON THE JOURNEY

The greatest gift we can give

the people in our lives is the gift of ourselves.

The Story of My Life is a journal that is ultimately

meant to be shared with family, friends, and loved ones.

As a road of reflection, this is a record of

your journey and it should reflect

the unique story of your life.

Discover the value, beauty, and meaning

you bring to this world.

*Oh that my words
were written!
Oh that they were inscribed
in a book!*

JOB 19:23

I dedicate this book to

_____

With love from

_____

In the year

_____

YOUR PHOTO HERE

*The accent of one's birthplace lingers in the mind
and in the heart as it does in one's speech.*

DUC DE LA ROCHEFOUCAULD

In the Beginning

My given name is _____

I was named for _____

Nicknames _____

Date of birth _____

Place of birth _____

Weight _____ Length _____

Hair color _____ Eyes _____

My Godparents _____

The initial mystery
that attends any journey is:
How did the traveller
reach his starting point
in the first place?

LOUISE BOGAN

My Family Tree

My mother _____ Birth date _____ Birth place _____

Her parents _____ Birth date _____ Birth place _____

_____

Her grandparents   Birth date   Birth place

_____

_____

_____

_____

My father _____ Birth date _____ Birth place _____

His parents _____ Birth date _____ Birth place _____

_____

His grandparents   Birth date   Birth place

_____

_____

_____

_____

My ancestors came from _____ in the year _____

_____

People will not look forward
to posterity
who never look backward
to their ancestors.

EDMUND BURKE

Family History

The origin of our family name _____
_____
_____
_____

The first members of our family to settle in this country were _____
_____
_____
_____

Where they settled and why _____
_____
_____
_____
_____
_____
_____
_____
_____
_____
_____
_____

YOUR PHOTO HERE

*To forget one's ancestors is to be a brook without a source,
a tree without a root.*

CHINESE PROVERB

Family History

Stories I've heard about my ancestors _____

_____

_____

_____

_____

_____

_____

How they earned their living _____

_____

_____

_____

_____

Hardships they endured _____

_____

_____

_____

_____

_____

_____

_____

_____

*It is of great importance
that the need for creating unity is recognized.
The human spirit is nourished
by a sense of connectedness.*

I Ching No. 8

Family Traditions

My favorite holiday _____

_____

_____

_____

_____

What it means to me _____

_____

_____

_____

_____

_____

_____

_____

_____

_____

_____

_____

_____

_____

YOUR PHOTO HERE

Life must be understood backwards.

SOREN KIERKEGAARD

Family Traditions

How we celebrate _____

_____

_____

_____

_____

_____

_____

_____

Other holidays we celebrate _____

_____

_____

_____

_____

_____

_____

_____

_____

_____

_____

Gastronomy is
and always has been
connected with its sister art
of love.

M.F.K. FISHER

Family Recipe for a Special Event

_____

_____

_____

_____

_____

_____

_____

_____

_____

_____

_____

_____

This recipe was given to me by _____

My memory of eating this _____

_____

_____

_____

_____

_____

Tell me what you eat
and I will tell you
what you are.

ANTHELME BRILLAT-SAVARIN

Family Recipe for a Special Event

_____

_____

_____

_____

_____

_____

_____

_____

_____

_____

_____

_____

_____

This recipe was given to me by _____

My memory of eating this _____

_____

_____

_____

_____

Reach into your memory
and look for what has restored you,
what helps you recover
from the sheer hellishness of life,
what food actually regenerates your system,
not so you can leap tall buildings
but so you can turn off the alarm clock
with vigor.

JIM HARRISON

Family Recipe for a Special Event

_____

_____

_____

_____

_____

_____

_____

_____

_____

_____

_____

This recipe was given to me by _____

My memory of eating this _____

_____

_____

_____

_____

_____

_____

_____

YOUR PHOTO HERE

Beginning as one loving whole, a single world,
mother and child will in time become separate beings;
just as lovers, beginning as two separate beings,
in time become one world, one whole.

DIANE ACKERMAN

My Mother

My mother's name _____

What I called her _____

Height _____ Weight _____ Hair _____ Eyes _____

How she looked to me _____
_____

Her vocation _____

What I admired about her _____
_____

My favorite memory of her _____
_____
_____
_____
_____
_____
_____
_____
_____

YOUR PHOTO HERE

My father was very sure about certain matters pertaining to the universe.
To him, all good things — trout as well as eternal salvation —
come by grace and grace comes by art and art does not come easy.

NORMAN MACLEAN

My Father

My father's name _____

What I called him _____

Height _____ Weight _____ Hair _____ Eyes _____

How he looked to me _____
_____

His vocation _____

What I admired about him _____
_____

My favorite memory of him _____
_____
_____
_____
_____
_____
_____
_____

No sooner met,
but they looked;
no sooner looked but they loved;
no sooner loved
but they sighed;
no sooner sighed
but they asked one another
the reason;
no sooner knew the reason
but they sought the remedy:
and in these degrees
have they made a pair
of stairs to marriage. . .

WILLIAM SHAKESPEARE

My Parents

How they met _____
_____
_____
_____
_____

Their wedding date _____

Where they were married _____

My favorite memory of them together _____
_____
_____
_____
_____

What I learned from them _____
_____
_____
_____
_____
_____
_____

God bless the roots!
Body and soul are one.

THEODORE ROETHKE

My Maternal Grandparents

My grandmother _____ My grandfather _____

How they met _____
_____
_____
_____
_____

Their wedding date _____

Where they were married _____

My favorite memory of them together _____
_____
_____
_____
_____

What I learned from them _____
_____
_____
_____
_____
_____

If the only prayer you say
in your whole life is
"Thank you,"
that would suffice.

MEISTER ECKHART

My Paternal Grandparents

My grandmother _____ My grandfather _____

How they met _____
_____
_____
_____
_____

Their wedding date _____

Where they were married _____

My favorite memory of them together _____
_____
_____
_____
_____

What I learned from them _____
_____
_____
_____

*For one human being to love another is perhaps
the most difficult task of all, the epitome, the ultimate test.
It is that striving for which all other striving
is merely preparation.*

RAINER MARIA RILKE

My Brothers and Sisters

Name _____ Birth date _____ Birth place _____

_____

_____

_____

_____

_____

My favorite memories of them _____

_____

_____

_____

Things we used to do _____

_____

_____

_____

A funny family story _____

_____

_____

_____

_____

Fate chooses your relations,
you choose your friends.

JAACQUES DELILLE

The Rest of the Family

My favorite relatives _____
_____
_____

My cousins _____
_____
_____

Things we used to do _____
_____
_____

The black sheep of our family _____
_____

A funny family story _____
_____
_____
_____
_____
_____
_____
_____

In my beginning is my end.

T.S. ELIOT

When I Was Young

Where I lived _____

From _____ to _____

Where I went to school _____

What I remember most is _____

_____

_____

_____

_____

Where I lived _____

From _____ to _____

Where I went to school _____

What I remember most is _____

_____

_____

_____

_____

God created man because
He loves a good story.

ELIE WIESEL

When I Was Young

Where I lived _____

From _____ to _____

Where I went to school _____

What I remember most is _____
_____
_____
_____
_____

Where I lived _____

From _____ to _____

Where I went to school _____

What I remember most is _____
_____
_____
_____
_____

YOUR PHOTO HERE

The advantage of living is not measured by length, but by use;
some men have lived long, and lived little:
attend to it while you are in it.

MICHEL EYQUEM DE MONTAIGNE

Where I Live Now

My home now _____
_____
_____
_____
_____
_____

How I got here _____
_____
_____
_____
_____
_____
_____
_____
_____
_____
_____
_____
_____
_____
_____
_____

I wake to sleep, and take my waking slow.

I feel my fate in what I cannot fear.

I learn by going where I have to go.

THEODORE ROETHKE

My Earliest Memories

Oft, in the stilly night,
Ere slumber's chain has bound me
Fond memory brings the light
of other days around me.

THOMAS MOORE

My Favorite Memories

The house where I grew up _____

_____

My bedroom _____

_____

Favorite hiding places _____

_____

My chores _____

_____

Family pets _____

_____

What I liked to do _____

_____

_____

_____

_____

_____

_____

Somehow
I had to send myself back,
with words as catalysts,
to open the memories up
and see what
they had to offer.

RAY BRADBURY

My Favorite Memories

Favorite games _____
_____

My favorite childhood book _____
_____

My favorite toys _____
_____

My favorite friend _____
_____

What I wanted to be when I grew up _____
_____

My first love _____
_____
_____
_____
_____
_____
_____
_____

Talent develops
in quiet places,
character
in the full current
of human life.

GOETHE

The World I Lived In

Popular music and dances _____

_____

_____

_____

_____

My favorite songs _____

_____

_____

_____

Newsmakers _____

_____

_____

_____

The price of things (milk, eggs, bread, stamps, gas . . .) _____

_____

_____

_____

_____

_____

Time is like a river
made up of the events which happen,
and its current is strong:
no sooner does everything appear
then it is swept away,
and another comes in its place,
and will be swept away too.

MARCUS AURELIUS

The World I Lived In

Fashions and fads _____
_____
_____
_____
_____

Inventions I've seen and how they've changed my life _____
_____
_____
_____
_____

The things I remember most _____
_____
_____
_____
_____
_____
_____
_____
_____
_____

Let yourself be silently drawn
by the stronger pull
of what you really love.

RUMI

What Influenced Me

Who has had the most influence on me and why _____
_____
_____
_____

Books that have influenced me _____
_____
_____
_____

Teachers that have influenced me _____
_____
_____
_____

Causes that I have worked for _____
_____
_____
_____
_____
_____
_____
_____

"Goodbye," said the fox.
"And now here is my secret,
a very simple secret:
It is only with the heart
that one can see rightly;
what is essential
is invisible to the eye."

ANTOINE de SAINT-EXUPERY

My Gifts to the World

My greatest accomplishment _____
_____
_____
_____

Because _____
_____
_____
_____

If I could I would change _____
_____
_____
_____

Something I've always wanted to do _____
_____
_____
_____
_____
_____
_____

Someday,
after we have mastered the winds,
the waves, the tides and gravity,
we shall harness
the energies of love.
Then, for the second time
in the history of the world,
we will have discovered fire.

PIERRE TEILHARD DE CHARDIN

My True Love

Name _____

How we met _____
_____
_____
_____

My first impression _____
_____
_____
_____

Our first date _____
_____
_____
_____

Our relationship _____
_____
_____
_____
_____
_____

*I shall become a master
in this art
only after a great deal
of practice.*

ERICH FROMM

Other Loves

_____

_____

_____

_____

_____

_____

_____

_____

_____

_____

My thoughts on love _____

_____

_____

_____

_____

_____

_____

_____

_____

_____

Home is where one starts from.

T.S. ELIOT

My First Child

Name _____ Nickname _____

Birth date _____ Birth place _____

Weight _____ Height _____ Hair _____ Eyes _____

On the day you were born _____

_____

_____

_____

_____

_____

Favorite memories _____

_____

_____

_____

_____

_____

_____

_____

_____

Not knowing

when the dawn will come

I open every door.

EMILY DICKINSON

My Second Child

Name _____ Nickname _____

Birth date _____ Birth place _____

Weight _____ Height _____ Hair _____ Eyes _____

On the day you were born _____
_____
_____
_____
_____
_____
_____

Favorite memories _____
_____
_____
_____
_____
_____
_____

From wonder into wonder.
Existence opens.

LAO-TSU

My Third Child

Name _____ Nickname _____

Birth date _____ Birth place _____

Weight _____ Height _____ Hair _____ Eyes _____

On the day you were born _____
_____
_____
_____
_____

Favorite memories _____
_____
_____
_____
_____
_____
_____
_____
_____
_____
_____

We all live under the same sky,
but we don't all have
the same horizon.

KONRAD ADENAUER

My Fourth Child

Name _____ Nickname _____

Birth date _____ Birth place _____

Weight _____ Height _____ Hair _____ Eyes _____

On the day you were born _____
_____
_____
_____
_____

Favorite memories _____
_____
_____
_____
_____
_____
_____
_____
_____
_____

YOUR PHOTO HERE

Friends are God's apology for relations.

HUGH KINGSMILL

My Friends

Name _____

How we met _____

Memories I'll cherish _____

_____

_____

_____

_____

_____

Name _____

How we met _____

Memories I'll cherish _____

_____

_____

_____

_____

_____

Friendship is a long conversation.
I suppose I could imagine a nonverbal friendship
revolving around shared physical work or sport,
but for me, good talk is the point of the thing.

PHILLIP LOPATE

My Friends

Name _____

How we met _____

Memories I'll cherish _____

_____

_____

_____

_____

_____

Name _____

How we met _____

Memories I'll cherish _____

_____

_____

_____

_____

_____

The meeting of two personalities
is like the contact
of two chemical substances:
If there is any reaction,
both are transformed.

C.G. JUNG

My Friends

Name _____

How we met _____

Memories I'll cherish _____

_____

_____

_____

_____

_____

Name _____

How we met _____

Memories I'll cherish _____

_____

_____

_____

_____

_____

Everyone has been made
for some particular work
and the desire for that work
has been put in his heart.

RUMI

My Professional Life

My profession _____
_____
_____

Where I went to school _____
_____
_____

Why I chose this profession _____
_____
_____

What I like most about it _____
_____
_____

What I dislike about it _____
_____
_____
_____
_____

Blessed is he
who has found his work.
Let him ask no other blessing.

THOMAS CARLYLE

My Professional Life

Professional accomplishments I'm proud of _____

_____

_____

_____

_____

_____

_____

_____

_____

_____

If I had to do it over again _____

_____

_____

_____

_____

_____

_____

_____

_____

_____

_____

_____

Thence we came to see the stars again.

DANTE

My Spiritual Life

My religion _____

I believe _____
_____
_____
_____
_____

What this means to me _____
_____
_____
_____
_____
_____
_____
_____
_____
_____
_____

I have been acquainted with the night.

ROBERT FROST

The Difficult Times

The most difficult time in my life _____

_____

_____

_____

_____

_____

How it changed me _____

_____

_____

_____

_____

_____

What I've learned from it _____

_____

_____

_____

_____

_____

_____

_____

What doesn't kill me makes me stronger.

ALBERT CAMUS

The Difficult Times

Another difficult time in my life _____

_____

_____

_____

_____

_____

How it changed me _____

_____

_____

_____

_____

_____

What I've learned from it _____

_____

_____

_____

_____

_____

_____

_____

Only the mediocre man is always at his best.

W. SOMERSET MAUGHAM

Mirror, Mirror on the Wall

What I like about myself and my life _____

_____

_____

_____

_____

_____

_____

_____

_____

_____

_____

What I'd like to change _____

_____

_____

_____

_____

_____

_____

_____

_____

_____

_____

YOUR PHOTO HERE

Yes: I am a dreamer.
For a dreamer is one who can find his way by moonlight,
and see the dawn before the rest of the world.

OSCAR WILDE

Hopes and Dreams

It took me a lifetime to learn that happiness is in quiet things, not the peaks of ecstasy.

ANAIS NIN

What Makes Me Happy

YOUR PHOTO HERE

What if we took more seriously this capacity of things to be close to us,
to reveal their beauty and expressive subjectivity? The result would be
a soul-ecology, a responsibility to the things of the world
based on appreciation and relatedness rather than on abstract principle.

THOMAS MOORE

My Favorite Possessions
(And why they're important to me)

_____

_____

_____

_____

_____

_____

_____

_____

_____

_____

_____

_____

_____

_____

_____

_____

_____

_____

_____

_____

_____

_____

Footfalls echo in the memory
Down the passage
which we did not take.

T.S. ELIOT

The Road Not Taken

How I thought my life would be different _____
_____
_____
_____
_____
_____
_____

Regrets _____
_____
_____
_____
_____
_____
_____
_____
_____
_____
_____
_____

"You have been my friend," replied Charlotte. "That in itself is a tremendous thing. I wove my webs for you because I liked you. After all, what's a life anyway? We're born, we live a little while, we die. A spider's life can't help being something of a mess, with all this trapping and eating flies. By helping you, perhaps I was trying to lift up my life a trifle. Heaven knows anyone's life can stand a little of that."

E.B. WHITE, CHARLOTTE'S WEB

Before I Die

Things I'd like to do _____

_____

_____

_____

_____

_____

_____

_____

_____

_____

_____

_____

_____

_____

_____

_____

_____

_____

_____

_____

_____

_____

Express yourself completely.
and then keep quiet.

TAO TE CHING

What I've Learned About Life

The master gives himself up
to whatever
the moment brings.

TAO TE CHING

How Others See Me

(To be written by family and friends)

_____

_____

_____

_____

_____

_____

_____

_____

_____

_____

_____

_____

_____

_____

_____

_____

_____

_____

_____

_____

_____

_____

YOUR PHOTO HERE

There is only one thing in the world worse than being talked about, and that is not being talked about.

OSCAR WILDE

How Others See Me

(To be written by family and friends)

_____

_____

_____

_____

_____

_____

_____

_____

_____

_____

_____

_____

_____

_____

_____

_____

_____

_____

_____

_____

Although to be driven back upon oneself
is an uneasy affair at best, rather like
trying to cross a border with borrowed credentials,
it seems to me now the one condition necessary
to the beginnings of real self-respect.

JOAN DIDION

How I'd Like to Be Remembered

It is not the answer that enlightens,
but the question.

EUGENE IONESCO

If I could take one memory with me into the afterlife, what would it be, and why?

_____

_____

_____

_____

_____

_____

_____

_____

_____

_____

_____

_____

_____

_____

_____

_____

_____

_____

_____

_____

_____

_____

On an occasion of this kind
it becomes more than a moral duty
to speak one's mind.
It becomes a pleasure.

OSCAR WILDE

Memories I'd Like to Share

Now is not the time
to think of what you do not have.
Think of what you can do
with what there is.

ERNEST HEMINGWAY

Memories I'd Like to Share

Knowing others is intelligence;

Knowing yourself is true wisdom.

TAO TE CHING

And Always Remember . . .

What a wonderful life I've had!
I only wish I'd realized it sooner.

COLETTE